Clarinet Exam Pieces

ABRSM Grade 2
Selected from the 2018–2021 syllabus

C000078393

Date of exam

Contents
page

Consultant Editor for ABRSM: David Blackwell
Footnotes: Dominic Wells

Other pieces for Grade 2

First published in 2017 by ABRSM (Publishing) Ltd,
a wholly owned subsidiary of ABRSM, 4 London Wall Place,
London EC2Y 5AU, United Kingdom
© 2017 by The Associated Board of the Royal Schools of Music
Distributed worldwide by Oxford University Press

Music origination by Julia Bovee
Cover by Kate Benjamin & Andy Potts
Printed in England by Page Bros (Norwich) Ltd,
on materials from sustainable sources.
Reprinted in 2019

Allegro

K. 3

Arranged by David Blackwell

W. A. Mozart
(1756–91)

This little Allegro was written for piano on 4th March 1762, and from the 'K.' (Köchel) catalogue number, we know that this is one of Mozart's earliest works – in fact, he was just six years old when he wrote it!

This arrangement by David Blackwell features the lowest or 'chalumeau' register of the clarinet. The elegant, legato phrasing (e.g. the pairs of quavers in bars 5–6) contrasts with the cheeky staccato notes (e.g. bar 7). Another feature is the many dynamic markings: sometimes these are sudden, such as the *p* in bar 8 following an *mf* passage; at other times they are more gradual (through a *crescendo*).

The Trout

 A:2

Arranged by Nancy Litten

Franz Schubert
(1797–1828)

Although Schubert died when he was just 31 years old, he managed to compose over 600 Lieder (German songs) in his brief lifetime. *Die Forelle* ('The Trout') is one of the most-loved and famous of all his songs – so famous in fact, that Schubert was commissioned to re-use the melody in a Piano Quintet, which became one of his most celebrated chamber pieces. This arrangement was inspired by both of these works.

The song tells the story of a person watching a trout swimming in a stream, before a fisherman catches it. Its light-hearted, humorous character is expressed through the phrasing – in particular the staccato notes and slurs – leading to a singing-like quality.

A:3

I Love My Love

Arranged by Alan Bullard

Trad. Cornish

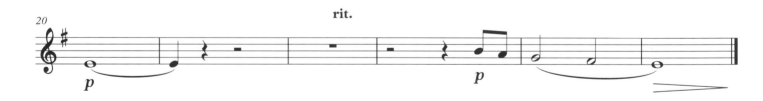

I Love My Love is a folk song from Cornwall, a picturesque county on the south-west tip of England. The Cornish cliffs look out to sea, and unsurprisingly the words of this song include seafaring images. It tells of a boy and a girl in love. One day the boy's parents send him off to sea, but eventually his boat returns and he is reunited with his beloved. Despite this happy ending, the piece has a mournful, longing quality, best served by legato playing, and shaping each phrase as if you were telling someone a story.

The song is perhaps more widely known today in an arrangement for choir by Gustav Holst: the composer of *The Planets*.

Oom-Pah-Pah

from Oliver!

B:1

Arranged by David Blackwell

Lionel Bart
(1930–99)

Taken from the popular musical, *Oliver!* (based on Charles Dickens's novel *Oliver Twist*), the song 'Oom-Pah-Pah' is sung by Nancy, a market-seller. She is one of the few characters who looks out for Oliver, a poor orphan who has become involved with a young gang of thieves. Nancy sings this song to distract the others, so that Oliver can escape to a better life with Mr Brownlow, a kind gentleman who adopts him.

In the musical, the setting for this song is a pub. At the start you play Nancy singing the verse, and when you reach the chorus (bar 21) imagine a lively crowd singing and swinging along with you!

B:2

Definitely!

No. 2 from *November Blues*

Mike Cornick
(born 1947)

The subtitle of this piece – No. 2 from *November Blues* – offers a clue about its character. The Blues is a type of jazz, and every bar shows the influence of this musical style, in particular the blue notes (notes flattened by a semitone) and swung quavers. A good sense of rhythm and especially pulse is important in this piece: notice how some of the phrases start on the beat, while others begin off the beat.

Mike Cornick studied composition at Trinity College of Music and is now best known for his jazz piano publications.

Getting to the Front of the Queue

Paul Harris

Being patient isn't always easy, especially when you have to wait in a queue – at the dentist; the cinema; the supermarket. That's what this piece is all about, so when playing it, take your time – don't rush, and don't skip ahead in the queue! The dynamic range might represent your mood along the way: perhaps the louder passage at bar 9 suggests becoming a little impatient, before calming down again a few bars later.

Paul Harris studied the clarinet at the Royal Academy of Music and is one of the UK's leading music educationalists, with over six hundred publications to his name.

C:1

Tenuto Study No. 9 in G

from 'Die einfachsten Vortragsarten' from *Elementarschule für Klarinette*

Friedrich Demnitz
(1845–90)

Friedrich Demnitz was a virtuoso clarinettist of the late 19th century. He is known by clarinet students all over the world for his *Elementarschule für Klarinette* (*Elementary School for Clarinet*) – a collection of studies focusing on different techniques of the instrument.

This particular study from 'Die einfachsten Vortragsarten' ('The simplest forms of phrasing') section aims to improve your tenuto playing. 'Tenuto' originates from the Latin word 'tenere', which means 'to hold'. Although not marked by tenuto marks ( ), all notes should be held for their full duration.

Castle Waltz

No. 8 from *21st-Century Clarinet Studies*

Colin Radford
(born 1959)

Before you start playing this piece, try to picture a castle in your mind. There's an old, grand ballroom, but it's not full of people; just two figures, dancing a waltz together. There's a slightly spooky feel to this dance. It's quiet, and the phrases are short, as if the dancers are pausing at the final crotchet of each phrase. At bar 9 the melody (now in a major key) is raised an octave higher. Here, the dancers relax a little, with a slightly louder dynamic and longer phrases, before returning to the more formal style of the opening. A *ritardando* draws the waltz to a graceful conclusion.

Colin Radford has performed as a clarinet soloist for the BBC and international radio and television, as well as having played with several London orchestras.

AB 3859

C:3

Continental Breakfast

James Rae
(born 1957)

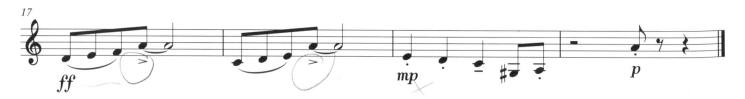

People often refer to a 'Continental breakfast' to distinguish it from an 'English breakfast'. Instead of sausages, eggs and bacon, you'd have toast, cereals and pastries. Articulation and dynamics really help bring out the character of this piece. Perhaps the tentative staccato notes at the beginning suggest tiptoeing downstairs without waking anyone up. At bar 5 you see all the food before you on the table, and by bar 9 you're gulping down your cereal. Four bars later (the *f*), toast is popping up and you're reaching out for the butter and jam. You've just room for one final mouthful, before tiptoeing away and gently closing the door behind you.

Having studied clarinet, bass clarinet, piano and composition at the Guildhall School of Music and Drama, James Rae has pursued a successful and varied career in music.